ISBN 978-1-952840-28-9

UNITED HOUSE Publishing
Clarkston, Michigan info@unitedhousepublishing.com
www.unitedhousepublishing.com

Cover and interior design: Amber Olafsson
Cover and interior illustrations: Megan Webber

Printed in the United States of America 2022—First Edition

SPECIAL SALES
Most UNITED HOUSE books are available at special quantity discounts when purchased in bulk by corporations, organizations, and special-interest groups. For information, please e-mail orders@unitedhousepublishing.com

*For Jack—who sings for joy when
he's excited, just like his mama.*

JOY TO THE WORLD
THE LORD IS COME

LET EARTH RECEIVE HER KING

LET EVERY HEART

PREPARE HIM ROOM

AND HEAVEN
AND NATURE SING

AND HEAVEN
AND NATURE SING

AND HEAVEN,
AND HEAVEN,
AND NATURE SING

JOY TO THE EARTH
THE SAVIOR REIGNS

LET MEN THEIR SONGS EMPLOY

WHILE FIELDS AND FLOODS

ROCKS, HILLS, AND PLAINS

REPEAT THE SOUNDING JOY

REPEAT THE SOUNDING JOY

REPEAT, REPEAT,
THE SOUNDING JOY

HE RULES THE WORLD

WITH TRUTH AND GRACE

AND MAKES
THE NATIONS PROVE

THE GLORIES OF HIS RIGHTEOUSNESS

AND WONDERS OF HIS LOVE

AND WONDERS OF HIS LOVE

AND WONDERS,
WONDERS,

OF HIS LOVE

PICTURE GLOSSARY

ANGELS

Angels were the first to proclaim the birth of Jesus. They appeared in the night sky to shepherds in the fields of Bethlehem and announced: "Don't be afraid!" the angel said. "I bring you good news that will bring great joy to all people. The Savior—yes, the Messiah, the Lord—has been born today in Bethlehem, the city of David!" Luke 2:10-11

NATIVITY

Nativity comes from the Latin word *nativitatis* meaning birth, and most commonly refers to the birth of Jesus Christ. Jesus is wrapped in swaddling cloths and placed in a manger, which is a trough animals eat from. Since there was no room in the inn, Mary gave birth to Jesus in the same place the innkeeper kept his animals.

HEAVEN & NATURE

God created the world in such a marvelous way that even the moon, sun, stars, fields, mountains, and rivers speak about how great He is. Nature is His handiwork. "The heavens declare the glory of God; the skies proclaim the work of his hands." Psalm 19:1

THE SAVIOR REIGNS

At Christmas, we celebrate the Savior who came, was born, and went to the cross in place of us, and now He reigns forever over all. "Now Jesus is far above any ruler or authority or power or leader or anything else—not only in this world but also in the world to come." Ephesians 1:21

NATIONS PROVE

As Jesus is revealed, "... the Sovereign LORD will make righteousness and praise spring up before all nations," Isaiah 61:11 says. This means as people all over the world, from every nation, believe in Jesus, they will be made righteous and be filled with praises of joy.

HIS RIGHTEOUSNESS

Jesus came to restore us back to the right relationship with God. This is cause for great joy and celebration! Because of what He did on the cross, if we believe in Him, we get to live with God forever and are counted righteous (right with God)! Isn't this glorious?! "This righteousness is given through faith in Jesus Christ to all who believe." Romans 3:22

WISE MEN

Wise men from the east, who read the signs in the sky announcing the birth of the Messiah, brought gifts to honor and show love to God's Son. At Christmas, we give gifts to those we love and honor and remember it was God who gave us the greatest gift of His Son. Did you know they were not at the nativity but arrived about 2 years after Jesus was born?

CANDY CANES

Even candy canes remind us of God's love. The shape represents a shepherd staff—Jesus is our loving, Good Shepherd, and the first people to worship Jesus were humble shepherds. The white stripe reminds us that Jesus was pure and sinless, and the red represents the blood He shed to forgive our sins.

JOY TO THE WORLD

ABOUT THE CREATORS

ISAAC WATTS

"Joy To The World" was written in 1719 by Isaac Watts. Watts was both an English minister and a hymn writer. Some of his most famous hymns include, "Oh God, Our Help In Ages Past" and "When I Survey The Wondrous Cross." Interestingly enough, "Joy To The World" was not written as a Christmas song at all but is actually about the second coming of Christ. Watts based this song on Psalm 98, and it was released in his collection of the *Psalms of David Imitated in the Language of the New Testament*. The musical arrangement that we are all familiar with was added to the lyrics in 1848 by the American composer Lowell Mason. According to Hymnary.org, "Joy To The World" has been the most-published Christmas hymn in North America.

AMBER OLAFSSON

Amber is a wife, mama, author, and publisher. She lives with her husband, three energetic kids, and an ever-growing list of farm animals in North Carolina. Reading books to her children before bed has always been a special way of connecting, and inspired *The Christmas Carol Series*. She hopes these books encourage parents to connect with their children and teach them the words to beloved Christmas songs. Follow the Olafsson family adventures on Instagram: @amberolafsson

MEGAN WEBBER

Megan is a wife, proud Mama to Olivia, and an illustrator. She has a passion for art and enjoys all things creative. Her family lives in Concord where, as an elementary school teacher, she developed a a love for children's literature. You can learn more about Megan and her family on Instagram: @mlduck

CPSIA information can be obtained
at www.ICGtesting.com
Printed in the USA
LVHW071401041222
734561LV00012B/565